D0311706

Jack Frost's
Ice Castle

Special thanks to
Fiona Phillipson, Kath Grimshaw
and Sarah Levison

ORCHARD BOOKS
338 Euston Road, London NW1 3BH
Orchard Books Australia
Level 17/207 Kent Street, Sydney, NSW 2000

First published in 2012 by Orchard Books

Fairy illustrations on pages 7–51 © Georgie Ripper.
All other illustrations © Orchard Books 2012, based on
underlying copyright owned by Georgie Ripper.

A CIP catalogue record for this book is available
from the British Library.

ISBN 978 1 40831 978 9

3 5 7 9 10 8 6 4

Printed in China

The paper and board used in this paperback are natural
recyclable products made from wood grown in sustainable
forests. The manufacturing processes conform to the
environmental regulations of the country of origin.

Orchard Books is a division of Hachette Children's Books,
an Hachette UK company

www.hachette.co.uk

ORCHARD

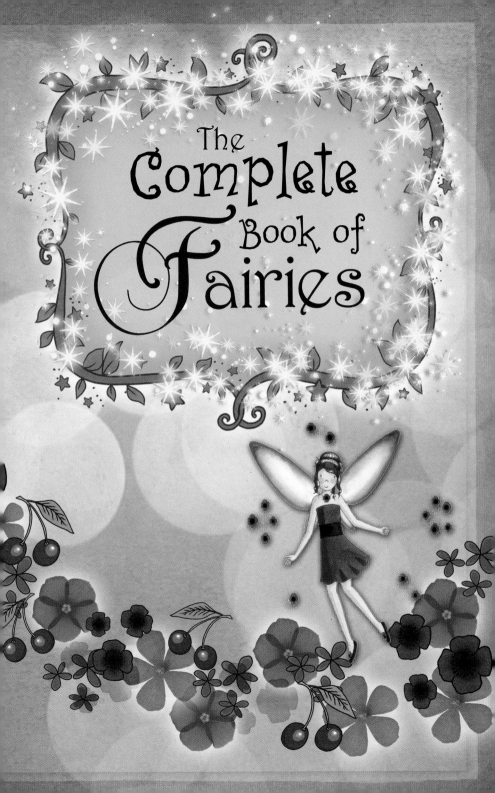

The Complete Book of Fairies

Contents

Ruby
the Red Fairy

Ruby is the fairy
that everyone knows.
She has roses in her hair and
on the tips of her toes!

Rainbow Reveal

Ruby's dress
is made from
hundreds of tiny
rose petals!

Ruby's favourite
foods are super-sweet
strawberries, and jam
tarts.

Did you know?

Some cultures
believe that the
colour red brings
luck and joy!

Ruby is very
special to
Rachel and Kirsty as
she's the very first fairy they
ever met! Ruby and her six
rainbow sisters were banished
from Fairyland by mean
Jack Frost's spell. Rachel
and Kirsty found Ruby by
following a beautiful rainbow
across Rainspell Island.

Amber
the Orange Fairy

Did you know?

The first oranges arrived in the UK in 1290. They were grown in Spain!

Rachel and Kirsty found Amber trapped in a seashell on the beach! They freed her with the help of a magical golden feather.

Rainbow Reveal

When Amber uses her wand it releases shimmering bubbles that smell of zingy oranges!

Saffron
the Yellow Fairy

Rainbow Reveal

Sparkly yellow butterflies emerge from Saffron's wand each time she waves it.

Did you know?

Honey bees beat their wings 200 times per second. That's 12,000 beats per minute!

Jack Frost's spell sent Saffron tumbling into a beehive! Luckily this friendly fairy had a lovely time with the bees and even made a very special bee friend called Queenie.

Fern
the Green Fairy

Rainbow Reveal

Fern's best friend is a grey squirrel called Fluffy!

There are 12 fairies who dress in different shades of green.

Fern's adventure took place in a secret garden! Rachel and Kirsty had to make their way through a maze to find Fern, watching out for some very naughty goblins. With the help of some friendly animals and a magical fairy firework, Fern was finally reunited with her rainbow sisters!

Did you know? The colour green is said to represent growth and harmony!

Did you know? Santa originally wore a green suit!

Sky
the Blue Fairy

Rachel and Kirsty had to scare off some ice-skating goblins to rescue Sky from a frozen rockpool. Sky was so cold her rainbow sisters needed to form a fairy ring to bring back her magical sparkles.

Whenever Sky waves her wand a shower of sparkling blue stars appears.

When fairies form a fairy ring their magic joins together and becomes very powerful!

Izzy's magic turns everything she touches a beautiful indigo colour!

Izzy
the Indigo Fairy

Izzy's adventure took place in the enchanted Land of Sweets! In this story the girls and Izzy met the Sugarplum Fairy and rode in a pink bubblegum balloon.

Did you know?
The beautiful Indigobird has indigo-coloured tail feathers.

Heather
the Violet Fairy

Rachel and Kirsty had to reunite Heather with her rainbow sisters before their holiday on Rainspell Island came to an end! Luckily, a magical ride on a merry-go-round led them to the little fairy. But then the fairies had to face cruel Jack Frost and his gang of goblins…

Did you know?

Rainbows appear when raindrops reflect sunlight.

Did you know?

A rainbow is a beautiful multicoloured arc of light in the sky.

Rainbow Reveal

Heather's magic allows her to create fizzing lilac bubbles. These can grow large enough to trap Jack Frost!

Crystal
the Snow Fairy

With one quick wave of a magical feather, these seven fairies can control the weather!

Because Jack Frost and his goblins had stolen the Weather Fairies' feathers, the weather in Fairyland and the human world turned totally topsy-turvy! Rachel and Kirsty had to help Crystal find her magical Snow Feather and return it to Doodle the weather-vane cockerel.

Rainbow Reveal

At the start of Crystal's story, Queen Titania gives Rachel and Kirsty two lockets filled with magical fairy dust.

The girls use this fairy dust in lots of their Rainbow Magic adventures!

Did you know?

The world's biggest snowman was built in Maine, USA, in 2008, and stood at over 37 metres tall!

Abigail
the Breeze Fairy

In the hands of a very naughty goblin, Abigail's breeze feather once caused chaos at the Wetherbury Village Fete. With the help of a plucky puppy called Twiglet, the girls and Abigail found the magical feather, high in the sky!

Rainbow Reveal

Breezy autumn is Abigail's favourite time of year – she loves to fly among the falling golden leaves!

Rainbow Reveal

Pearl's favourite colour is pale pink, the colour of sunsets.

Pearl
the Cloud Fairy

The magic of the cloud feather made everyone very grumpy when it was taken from its rightful fairy owner, Pearl!

Did you know?

Non-magical clouds are made up of very tiny droplets of water or ice crystals.

Goldie
the Sunshine Fairy

Goldie really is a little ray of sunshine! She's super-smiley, warm-hearted and full of giggles.

Did you know?

The sun is actually a star! It's the closest star to Earth, and is nearly 5 billion years old.

Did you know?

The city of Yuma in the USA is the sunniest place on Earth. There, the sun shines 94% of the time!

Everyone loves the sunshine! But when Goldie's magic sunshine feather was stolen from Doodle the weather-vane cockerel, the sun shone so much that it was far too hot in Wetherbury.

Evie
the Mist Fairy

Evie's mist feather creates sparkly wisps of mist that make things look very pretty! But in the hands of a naughty goblin, the feather can cause all sorts of misty mischief.

Rainbow Reveal

Fairy children love to play hide and seek in Evie's mist! Goblins are scared of mist as they think Pogwurzels will be able to sneak up behind them!

Storm
the Lightning Fairy

Rachel and Kirsty had a very dramatic adventure with Storm the Lightning Fairy! They came face to face with a mean goblin and Storm's powerful lightning feather, inside a dusty old museum.

Did you know?

Lightning is a bright flash of electricity produced by a thunderstorm.

Hayley
the Rain Fairy

Because horrid Jack Frost had stolen her magical rain feather, in Hayley's adventure the rain just wouldn't stop falling! With Hayley's help, the girls paddled through a flood to return all seven magical weather feathers to Doodle.

Rainbow Reveal

Hayley's favourite film is 'Singing in the Rain'!

Did you know?

Rain is recycled water that evaporated from the world's lakes, rivers and oceans!

Cherry
the Cake Fairy

Cherry the Cake Fairy loves to bake The most delicious party cakes!

Queen Titania and King Oberon's 1,000th jubilee was a very happy occasion, and the Party Fairies were on hand to make the celebrations extra special! But mean Jack Frost was determined to spoil the fun. Rachel and Kirsty had to help Cherry find her missing party bag so she could bake a magical cake fit for the royal couple!

Cherry's frilly red skirt looks just like an upside-down fairy cake case!

Rainbow Reveal

Did you know?

Cherry loves all cakes but her very favourite is a cherry jam tart. Yummy!

Melodie
the Music Fairy

Goblins love music. But the silly creatures are actually tone-deaf and have no sense of rhythm!

Poor Kirsty's ballet show was almost ruined when a naughty goblin stole Melodie's party bag and caused musical mayhem!

With a wave of Melodie's wand, instruments start to play all by themselves!

Grace
the Glitter Fairy

Grace's favourite party foods are Cherry's fairy cakes – covered in edible glitter!

When Grace's magical bag went missing, all glittery party decorations lost their sparkle.

Honey
the Sweet Fairy

Did you know?

Honey is made by honey bees. These bees communicate with one another by dancing!

N o party is complete without some delicious sweet treats. Honey's adventure took place in Mrs Twist's Sweet Shop, which is full of all the sweets you could ever dream of! But when a goblin tried to snatch Honey's party bag, the shop got into a very sticky situation.

Rainbow Reveal

Honey and her fairy helpers love inventing new sweets. They have lots of fun trying out their creations on the other Party Fairies!

Polly
the Party Fun Fairy

Polly the Party Fun Fairy makes sure that every party has brilliant games for everyone to enjoy! So it was very important that the girls helped Polly to find her party bag when it went missing.

Rainbow Reveal

When Polly uses the fairy dust in her party bag, beautiful blue balloons appear!

Polly's very favourite party game is Pass the Magic Parcel.

Phoebe
the Fashion Fairy

Phoebe makes sure that everyone looks fairy fabulous at parties and celebrations, with fashionable frocks and amazing accessories!

Rainbow Reveal

The silk used to make Phoebe's dress is from magical silkworms. The dress glimmers and shimmers in every light!

Jasmine
the Present Fairy

**People have
been giving each other
presents for many hundreds
of years. It is likely the
tradition goes back to
Roman times.**

Jasmine's magic makes presents and prizes perfect for everyone! This special magical power has to be looked after very carefully. So when they met Jasmine, Rachel and Kirsty had to protect her bag and get to the King and Queen's 1,000th jubilee party on time.

Rainbow Reveal

**At the end of the
Party Fairies' stories,
Rachel and Kirsty are
each given a musical
jewellery box by the
fairy king and queen.**

**Jasmine is named
after a delicate,
beautifully scented
flower.**

India
the Moonstone Fairy

Nasty Jack Frost stole
each fairy's jewel,
So that his evil deeds
their magic could fuel!

The Jewel Fairies each have a precious stone. India's beautiful moonstone helps to make sure that everyone has sweet dreams. When Jack Frost stole the seven magical jewels, Rachel and Kirsty had to help the Jewel Fairies return them to Queen Titania's tiara – or all fairy magic would have faded away!

Rainbow Reveal

It is believed that moonstones bring good luck.

Did you know?

The glowing shimmer that surrounds the moonstone is said to resemble moonlight.

Rainbow Reveal

When all of the Jewel Fairies' jewels are in Queen Titania's tiara, a magical rainbow is formed once a year. The fairies use this to recharge their magic!

Scarlett
the Garnet Fairy

Scarlett's jewel has the power to make things bigger and smaller, so in her story it was very important that her garnet was returned to the tiara. Otherwise Kirsty and Rachel might have stayed tiny forever!

Rainbow Reveal

Scarlett and Ruby once held a party where everyone had to dress in red!

Emily
the Emerald Fairy

Emily's adventure took place in a wonderful toy shop! But with the missing jewel affecting Emily's special ability to see into the future, things were not always what they seemed…

Did you know?

If you were born in May, then the deep-green emerald is your birthstone!

Chloe
the Topaz Fairy

Chloe's golden topaz went missing at Halloween, one of the most mystical times of year... With Chloe's magical jewel missing, her ability to change one thing into something else caused all kinds of tricks and treats at a fancy-dress shop in Tippington.

Rainbow Reveal

Chloe's jewel is a beautiful golden colour, but topaz can actually come in many different colours!

Did you know?

The Queen of England's Crown Jewels contain 23,578 precious stones.

24

Amy
the Amethyst Fairy

Amy's magical amethyst controls appearing and disappearing magic – she can make things invisible! When Amy's jewel went missing, the girls had a very odd adventure, high up in a treehouse!

Rainbow Reveal

Amy sometimes uses her magic to help Polly the Party Fun Fairy with her party games!

Sophie
the Sapphire Fairy

Rainbow Reveal

Sophie is a great friend of Zara the Starlight Fairy. The sapphires that flow from Sophie's wand look so beautiful in Zara's starlight!

Sophie's sparkling sapphire looks after wishing magic! With her jewel lost in the human world, wishes everywhere were in a terrible muddle…

Jewel Fairies

Lucy
the Diamond Fairy

In the final Jewel Fairies adventure, Rachel and Kirsty travelled to Fairyland to help Lucy find her diamond, which controls flying magic. The girls had to avoid scary Jack Frost's ice bolts so they could return the diamond to Queen Titania's tiara!

Rainbow Reveal

Kirsty and Rachel see a huge, glittering diamond just before they meet Elizabeth the Jubilee Fairy. This diamond is called the Great Star of Africa.

The girls love flying but Kirsty sometimes finds it a bit scary, especially when she's a fairy and Jack Frost is chasing her!

Did you know?

This precious jewel can be found in a variety of colours, even black!

Katie
the Kitten
Fairy

Katie's the fairy with a cute magic kitten, One purr from Shimmer, and you will be smitten!

The Pet Keeper Fairies make sure that all pets in Fairyland and the human world have happy homes. But when the seven magical pets were kidnapped, the fairies' magic stopped working!
Rachel and Kirsty love animals and were happy to try and reunite the fairies with their beloved pets in the seven Pet Keeper Fairies adventures.

Rainbow Reveal

Kirsty has a gorgeous kitten called Pearl.

There are three fairies who have cute pet cats!

Did you know?

All kittens are born with blue eyes. They don't develop their true eye colour until they are about three months old!

Bella
the Bunny Fairy

If ever a bunny is in trouble, it's Bella to the rescue! Her enchanted helper is a fluffy rabbit called Misty who twitches her nose and is always changing colour.

Rainbow Reveal

Misty lives in a cosy burrow underneath Bella's pretty toadstool house.

Did you know?

A baby rabbit is called a kit!

Georgia
the Guinea Pig Fairy

Did you know?

Wild guinea pigs live in South America!

Rainbow Reveal

Guinea pigs are very sociable animals. Sparky loves to play with all the other magic pets!

Georgia's adventure took place on Strawberry Farm. Rachel and Kirsty had to deal with some very odd sheep to reunite Georgia and her super-cute guinea pig, Sparky!

Lauren
the Puppy Fairy

Rachel has a dog called Buttons!

The girls were having a wonderful time at the Wetherbury Spring Fair when they met Sunny, Lauren's magic puppy. But it was a race against time to reunite him with Lauren before some bouncing goblins could snatch him!

Did you know?
The biggest number of puppies ever born in a litter was 24!

Rainbow Reveal

In Fairyland, pets choose their owners – not like in the human world where it's the other way round!

Harriet
the Hamster Fairy

Three naughty goblins set a tricky trap for Twinkle the magic hamster in Harriet's adventure. Kirsty and Rachel had to reach him before the goblins could!

Molly
the Goldfish Fairy

There were some very cunning goblins disguised as gnomes in Molly's story. And they stole Flash, Molly's magic goldfish! Luckily, Flash was very clever and managed to swim back to Molly.

Penny
the Pony Fairy

Did you know?
There are over 300 different breeds of horse in the world. A pony is a small horse measuring under 14.2 hands high.

Rachel and Kirsty were having a lovely pony ride in the forest when Glitter the magic pony arrived in a twinkle of fairy magic! Unfortunately a gang of seven goblins threatened to spook all the ponies with their mischievous ways. And then Jack Frost arrived…

Rainbow Reveal

Both Rachel and Kirsty love horseriding. They have more horsey fun with Helena the Horseriding Fairy!

Pet Keeper Fairies

31

Megan
the Monday Fairy

Megan and her sisters each have a magic flag, But when the flags go missing, every day's a drag!

Rainbow Reveal

Every morning, Francis the Royal Time Guard looks in the Fairyland Book of Days to check which day it is.

When the girls met Megan, it turned out that Jack Frost had been up to his old tricks again! With their seven magical flags missing, the Fun Day Fairies couldn't make any day anywhere enjoyable. They had to find their flags and charge their wands – or lose their magical powers for ever and ever…

Did you know?

The word Monday comes from an ancient Anglo-Saxon word meaning 'the moon's day'.

Tallulah
the Tuesday Fairy

With Tallulah's magical flag missing, this pretty fairy couldn't help anyone have a good time on a Tuesday! That meant that Rachel's sports day was no fun at all.

Rainbow Reveal

Tallulah is great friends with Tia the Tulip Fairy. These two little fairies love to fly around Fairyland together!

Willow
the Wednesday Fairy

Rainbow Reveal

Willow's flag is one of the prettiest of them all. It's green and gold, and covered in glitter.

In this adventure, Rachel and Kirsty had to find Willow's flag at the Tippington Arts and Crafts Fair. The trouble was that it was the perfect place for naughty goblins to hide!

Thea
the Thursday Fairy

Did you know?

Every year in America, Thanksgiving Day takes place on the fourth Thursday of November.

Thea's story took place in an aquarium! It was a magical place for the girls to visit – there were sea horses, crabs, sharks, otters and a reef to see… Oh, and some troublesome goblins were there too, and they wanted Thea's fun day flag!

Rainbow Reveal

Kirsty and Rachel love to speed through the water with their fairy friends! Fairy magic makes them warm and dry as soon as they're back on land.

Thea's favourite thing to do on a Thursday morning is to teach young fairies how to dance a fairy jig!

Freya
the Friday Fairy

Rainbow Reveal

Freya is very arty and teaches the other Fun Day Fairies how to paint pretty pictures.

Everyone loves Fridays – but when Freya's beautiful lilac flag went missing, no one in either the fairy or human worlds had that fun Friday feeling!

Sienna
the Saturday Fairy

Rainbow Reveal

All of the Fun Day Fairies' flags have a picture of the sun on them. Everyone feels full of sunshine and happiness when the flags are working their magic!

Even a fabulous fashion show couldn't make the Saturday in Sienna's story fun! Luckily, her flag was somewhere backstage at the show – but so were a gang of thieving goblins…

Sarah
the Sunday Fairy

Sunday is traditionally known as a day of rest, but there was no rest for Rachel and Kirsty in this final Fun Day adventure. A picnic at Windy Lake was the girls' last chance to reunite Sarah with her magic flag. But first they had to persuade a frosty visitor to help them!

Rainbow Reveal

At the end of the Fun Day adventures, Queen Titania gave Rachel and Kirsty a glittering kite each! Each time they fly with their kites the girls think of their fairy friends.

Phoebe the Fashion Fairy uses her magic to change the colours of Sarah's stripy tights for special occasions!

Did you know?

Sunday is known as both the first, and the last, day of the week! It just depends on what religion you follow.

Tia
the Tulip Fairy

When the magic petals are taken away, No flowers can bloom to brighten each day...

The Petal Fairies make sure that flowers everywhere grow beautifully, bringing lots of happiness and joy to everyone! But when Jack Frost stole the petals and scattered them around the human world, Rachel and Kirsty had a tough job to return Tia's tulip petal to her...

Did you know?
Tulips come in a huge variety of colours, including red, purple and orange.

Rainbow Reveal
Jack Frost secretly wishes he had green fingers. He wants pretty flowers to grow in his icy garden!

Pippa
the Poppy Fairy

Pippa's adventure took place in a pretty flower shop, but with the magic petals missing, all the flowers were droopy! The girls had to outwit a whole gang of naughty goblins to find Pippa's poppy petal and return it to Fairyland.

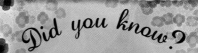

Did you know?

Bright red poppies are worn by many people each November to remember those who have fought in wars.

Louise
the Lily Fairy

Did you know?
In Chinese culture the lily means 'forever in love'!

In this story, Rachel and Kirsty row a boat on a lovely lake full of lily pads! But with Louise's magic petal in the hands of the pesky goblins, the lily pads had no flowers…

Charlotte
the Sunflower Fairy

Charlotte's cheery sunflower is a firm fairy favourite. When Jack Frost took her magic petal, everyone was very unhappy to see her stunning flowers wilting. So it was very important that Rachel and Kirsty helped this pretty little fairy get her petal back so her flowers could stand tall in the sunshine once more!

Did you know?
Sunflowers are very easy to grow! Plant each seed in a sunny and sheltered place in the garden. Water well and in about two weeks you'll see sunflower shoots coming up. Magical!

Rainbow Reveal
Even though Charlotte looks after yellow sunflowers, her favourite colour is blue!

Olivia
the Orchid Fairy

The orchid is a very delicate flower. When they met Olivia, Rachel and Kirsty had to help her get her pretty blue and purple petal back from the goblins before the clumsy creatures destroyed it.

Rainbow Reveal

Each magic petal protects a certain type of flower, but all the petals look after every other flower and plant in the world, too!

Danielle
the Daisy Fairy

Did you know?

The name 'Daisy' comes from the Old English word meaning 'day's eye' – because daisies open at dawn!

In her adventure, Danielle and the girls had to dodge a storm of icy hailstones to get her magic petal back from the mean goblins! Luckily, the fairy friends had some help from a very long, magical daisy chain!

Ella
the Rose Fairy

Did you know?
There are over 100 different species of rose!

A flower show set in some beautiful gardens was where Kirsty and Rachel had their adventure with Ella the Rose Fairy! In this final Petal Fairies story, the girls had to flutter through Chaney Court Hedge Maze, and come face to face with chaos-causing goblins, to find Ella's beautiful petal.

Rainbow Reveal

When it's the other Petal Fairies' birthdays, Ella sews together fallen rose petals to make pretty gifts.

Bethany
the Ballet Fairy

The Dance Fairies
love to sway and to move,
But without their ribbons,
the world's lost its groove!

Rainbow Reveal

In this story,
Kirsty and Rachel are
going to see Swan Lake,
a very famous ballet
about a swan princess.

Rainbow Reveal

Bethany teaches the little
Rainbow Magic fairies how
to dance. They look very
sweet practising their pliés
in tiny fairy tutus!

All seven Dance Fairies were cast into the human world by dastardly Jack Frost, and he took their magic ribbons! Nobody could enjoy dancing in the human world or in Fairyland until Rachel and Kirsty helped the fairies get their ribbons back.

Jade
the Disco Fairy

Jade is a real disco star in her swirly green hipsters and funky top! In her story, it was the day of Kirsty's school disco. But although Jade looks ready to hit the dance floor, with her magical ribbon missing nobody was in the party mood…

Rainbow Reveal

Silly Jack Frost stole the Dance Fairies' ribbons because he wanted his goblin servants to dance well at his party!

Rebecca
the Rock 'n' Roll Fairy

Did you know?

Rock 'n' roll dancing is very energetic, with lots of jumps, throws and lifts.

Kirsty's parents were going to a rock 'n' roll dance in this adventure, but the girls knew that if Rebecca's ribbon wasn't returned to her quickly, the dance would be a disaster…

Dance Fairies

43

Tasha
the Tap Dance Fairy

Rachel and Kirsty were at an open day at Wetherbury College in this adventure when a gang of toe-tapping goblins attracted their attention! The girls and Tasha had to work out a cunning plan to distract the goblins so they could return the magic ribbon to its rightful owner.

Rainbow Reveal

Tasha loves to perform in front of her fairy friends. Sometimes she teams up with Leah the Theatre Fairy, and together they put on a great show!

Did you know?

The 'tap' of tap dance comes from metal sections that are fitted into the toes and heels of the special shoes. This makes them tap on the floor!

Jessica
the Jazz Fairy

Rainbow Reveal

Jessica's beautiful pink dress is a chic 1920s style. Her loose-fitting outfit means she can perform high kicks and splits.

The girls were invited to a grown-up party in this story, with a cool jazz band. But Rachel and Kirsty knew that because Jessica's magic ribbon was missing, disaster would soon strike!

Saskia
the Salsa Fairy

Did you know?
Salsa dancing originated in Cuba.

Rainbow Reveal

At Wetherbury Fiesta, the children play with a piñata. This is a papier-mâché decoration, filled with sweets. It's hung up and guests hit it with a stick until it opens!

Fun-loving Saskia brings every celebration to life with her super-cool Latin dance! But with her dance ribbon missing, the girls were worried that the Wetherbury Fiesta would be a disaster…

Dance Fairies

45

Imogen
the Ice Dance Fairy

Rainbow Reveal

Imogen and Poppy the Piano Fairy are great friends. Poppy creates magical tinkling tunes for Imogen to skate along to!

Did you know?
Ice dance is a form of figure skating. It's been part of the Winter Olympics since 1924.

This icy adventure starred seven ice-skating goblins! The pesky creatures caused chaos at the Glacier Ice Rink and ruined the show for everyone. The final dance ribbon had to be returned to Imogen, before any more disasters took place.

Helena
the Horseriding Fairy

It's time once again
for the games to start,
But with seven things lost,
no one can take part!

Rachel and Kirsty were about to go horseriding when they were magically whisked to Fairyland and introduced to seven new fairy friends! The Sporty Fairies were in trouble – Jack Frost's goblins had stolen the seven magical sporty objects. With these missing, the Fairy Olympics couldn't begin, and no one could enjoy any sports!

Rainbow Reveal

The Fairy Olympics are held in the Fairyland Arena, a magical place that changes to suit whichever sport is being played!

Rainbow Reveal

The winner of the Fairy Olympics is awarded a magnificent golden cup full of luck. Jack Frost really wants to get his hands on this!

Francesca
the Football Fairy

In Francesca's story, the girls went to watch a Tippington Rovers football match with Rachel's mum and dad! But some naughty goblins were also at the football ground, and they had Francesca's magic football…

Did you know?
In the USA, football is known as soccer!

Zoe
the Skating Fairy

With Zoe's magic shoelace missing, all skaters and skateboarders were in trouble! In this exciting adventure, it was up to the girls to help find the lace. Then Zoe could make skating fun again!

Did you know?
There is a sport called roller derby, where two teams skate round a rink together, and try to score points!

Naomi
the Netball Fairy

N etball is normally a fun and popular team sport, but with Naomi's magic netball missing, nobody was having a good time! Whilst helping Naomi, Rachel and Kirsty met a team called 'The Mean Green Netball Team'. The girls were very suspicious! Green normally means goblins, and goblins mean trouble…

Did you know?
Netball is similar to basketball in many ways, and it is thought to have developed from basketball!

Rainbow Reveal

Naomi's favourite netball position is Goal Attack.

Samantha
the Swimming Fairy

Rainbow Reveal

Normally, goblins don't like getting wet, but with Samantha's magic goggles close by, they have loads of fun swimming!

Swimming is the perfect sport to enjoy on a summer day! But with Samantha's magic goggles missing, Kirsty and Rachel had to be on high alert when they went for a dip at Aqua World!

Alice
the Tennis Fair

In Alice's exciting story, Tippington Tennis Club was taken over by troops of tennis-playing goblins! Rachel and Kirsty had the tricky task of helping Alice to get her magic racquet back.

Rainbow Reveal

Alice has lots of different tennis outfits but the white dress with sparkly pink accessories is her favourite!

Gemma
the Gymnastics Fairy

Did you know? The word gymnastics comes from an ancient Greek word meaning 'to exercise'.

Rainbow Reveal

By the time Kirsty and Rachel met Gemma properly, it was almost time for the Fairy Olympics to begin! Gemma's magic hoop was missing, and must be returned to Fairyland – otherwise Jack Frost and his goblins could still win the games and cause lots of trouble with the golden Fairyland Olympics Cup.

The Sporty Fairies are trying to teach the goblins a very important lesson – you don't have to cheat to enjoy sport!

Poppy
the Piano Fairy

Kirsty and Rachel love listening to music! So they were shocked to learn that music everywhere could be ruined because Jack Frost had stolen all of the magic musical instruments from the Royal School of Music. In Poppy's story, the Ice Lord formed a band with his goblins and was going to enter a music contest in the human world. The girls had to stop him!

The magical instruments must be found, For without them all music makes a horrible sound!

Rainbow Reveal

Jack Frost's group, Frosty's Gobolicious Band, play at the goblin party in Elizabeth the Jubilee Fairy's story.

Ellie
the Guitar Fairy

Ellie just loves playing funky tunes on her electric guitar! But when it was in the hands of the naughty goblins in the human world, even she couldn't play a note without it sounding awful…

Did you know?

There are two main types of guitar: acoustic and electric.

Fiona
the Flute Fairy

Fiona the Flute Fairy fluttered magically out of a sparkly card at the start of this story! She knew her magic flute was nearby, but had to ask for help from Rachel and Kirsty so she could get it back before the goblins caused more trouble.

Rainbow Reveal

The enchanting music that comes from Fiona's flute makes people want to follow it!

Danni
the Drum Fairy

Rachel and Kirsty were going to star in a pop video in this story! They were so excited but they also knew they had to stay alert if they were to find another missing magical musical instrument. Luckily the silly goblins soon appeared with Danni's magic drumsticks…

Rainbow Reveal

The Music Fairies' instruments are still fairy-size in the human world, so they can be very hard to spot!

Whenever Danni uses her wand, lots of tiny drumsticks appear!

Did you know?

Danni the Drum Fairy is the only fairy not holding her wand on her book cover!

Maya
the Harp Fairy

Maya's elegant harp plays magical musical melodies! But with the magic harp missing, harp music everywhere always sounds awful. Rachel and Kirsty had to help Maya find her instrument before their friend's wedding was ruined…

Rainbow Reveal

The earliest harps can be traced back to 3000 BC.

Victoria
the Violin Fairy

The girls had a sneak peek at Frosty's Gobolicious Band in this fairy tale! With Victoria's magic violin nearby to keep them in harmony, the band sounded great. But the girls had to return the violin to Victoria so all music could be harmonious.

Did you know?

The modern violin is made from over 70 pieces of wood!

Sadie
the Saxophone Fairy

Sadie's story was the final Music Fairies adventure, and it was time for the National Talent Competition! With Sadie's saxophone missing, the girls knew that Frosty's Gobolicious Band could easily win the competition, putting Fairyland in danger. Kirsty and Rachel had to work hard and save the day, without ruining the competition for everyone!

Rainbow Reveal

Even when the talent competition is over, Jack Frost still thinks he is a super-talented pop star!

Did you know?

The saxophone is made in about eight different sizes. That's not including fairy-size!

Ashley
the Dragon Fairy

The magical animals are lost in our world. They really need help from two special girls!

Ashley's young dragon is called Sizzle. He looks after the magical power of imagination.

Rachel and Kirsty were away for a week at an outdoor adventure camp when they met the Magical Animal Fairies. They discovered that Jack Frost had stolen seven young magical animals. The baby animals were all being trained to use a particular type of magic, so they could help everyone enjoy life. The animals escaped Jack Frost's icy clutches — but then got lost in the human world!

When Sizzle sneezes, small flames appear. All of Fairyland must watch out when the baby dragon has a cold!

Ashley has a Chinese dragon on the leg of her combats. This type of dragon is said to ward off evil spirits!

Magical Animal Fairies

Lara
the Black Cat Fairy

During a camp activity, Rachel and Kirsty found Lara's magical animal. Lucky, an adorable little black cat, has the power to bring good luck. But as bad luck was happening *everywhere*, the girls did their best to get the pretty kitty back to Lara.

Did you know?

Some cultures think that black cats bring good luck, and others think they bring bad luck!

Erin
the Firebird Fairy

Did you know?

Another name for the firebird is the phoenix.

In Erin's adventure, the girls spotted a very unusual bird by the stream! It was Giggles the Firebird, whose magic looks after humour. Rachel, Kirsty and Erin had to try and reach Giggles before the goblins got hold of him.

Rihanna
the Seahorse Fairy

Rihanna's magic seahorse, Bubbles, looks after friendship – which is very important to both fairies and humans! When Bubbles isn't in Fairyland with his fairy keeper, friendships everywhere suffer. So when Jack Frost stole Bubbles, Rachel and Kirsty had to find the little seahorse and reunite him with Rihanna.

Rainbow Reveal

Normally seahorses live in certain oceans, but as Bubbles is a magic seahorse he can swim in lakes and rivers, too!

Rihanna's magic allows the girls to breathe underwater!

Did you know?
Seahorse dads have babies, not the mums!

Sophia
the Snow Swan Fairy

The girls were on a night-time walk at camp when a shimmering swan caught their eye! They had to cross a beautiful waterfall and reach Sophia's baby swan before the goblins did.

Rainbow Reveal

Sophia's magic power is to spread compassion.

Leona
the Unicorn Fairy

Leona's magical animal is Twisty the baby unicorn – he looks like a white pony! Twisty's magic came in very handy when Rachel's wrist was hurt by the actions of a careless goblin.

Rainbow Reveal

Leona and Helena the Horseriding Fairy spend hours plaiting the manes of their horsey friends!

Caitlin
the Ice Bear Fairy

Mean Jack Frost stole the Magical Animals because he knew the world would be a miserable place without them.

It was a chilly final day at the adventure camp and the girls had a big hill to climb! From the top of the hill they were hoping to spot the final missing magical animal, Crystal the ice-bear cub. But Jack Frost was also nearby with his frosty magic, hoping to find the little bear first…

Did you know?

A polar bear's fur isn't white! Each hair is a hollow tube that reflects light. It also traps the sun's heat to help keep the polar bear warm.

When they're born, polar bears are the size of a mouse!

Magical Animal Fairies

Nicole
the Beach Fairy

These seven fairies keep
the world clean,
Safe from the Ice Lord,
who's nasty and mean!

In the Green Fairies' adventures, Rachel and Kirsty asked the fairies for *their* help! They returned to Rainspell Island for a holiday and were very upset to see that the beautiful beach was covered in litter. They knew they needed some magic to help them clean up the environment and show others how to do the same. But the last thing Jack Frost wanted were more interfering fairies…

Rainbow Reveal

The goblins steal the Green Fairies' wands. Without them the fairies can only do a certain amount to help the planet.

At the start of these seven stories, the Green Fairies are still in training!

Isabella
the Air Fairy

It's Isabella's job to make sure that the air humans and fairies breathe is as clean as possible! In her adventure, Isabella asked Rachel and Kirsty to help her clean up Seabury's air.

Did you know? **The cleanest air in the world is on the island of Tasmania and in Antarctica.**

Edie
the Garden Fairy

Gardens are such important places! They provide safe homes for lots of wildlife and plants. When Rachel and Kirsty met Edie, they all volunteer to create a special garden. But Jack Frost had other plans…

Rainbow Reveal

Edie's mum was head gardener for the royal fairy household!

Coral
the Reef Fairy

Did you know?

Every coral reef is a living organism! Reefs are very delicate and easily damaged by human touch or polluted water.

The world's biggest reef is the Great Barrier Reef in Australia. It is so long it can be seen from space!

Coral joined the girls for a wonderful underwater adventure in this story! The girls magically travelled to a warm, tropical ocean many hundreds of miles away from Rainspell Island. They had to help Coral teach an important lesson to some very destructive goblins.

Rainbow Reveal

Coral's emerald ankle bracelets were a birthday gift from the Jewel Fairies.

Lily
the Rainforest Fairy

Did you know?

Rainforests contain more living creatures than any other place on Earth! So it is very important that they are protected.

The girls were on a nature walk on Rainspell Island when, with the help of Lily's fairy magic, they were whisked to an exotic rainforest. They met a host of amazing exotic creatures!

Milly
the River Fairy

Rainbow Reveal

Milly and Hayley the Rain Fairy are the very best of friends. These water-loving fairies love to splash around in rivers and puddles!

Milly had to get her wand back from Jack Frost so she could make all rivers clean and healthy once more. But first she needed the girls to help her outwit the goblins…

Carrie
the Snow Cap Fairy

Carrie's adventure was the last in the Green Fairies series! Rachel and Kirsty had only one wand left to find but Jack Frost was determined to hang onto it, leading to a showdown amongst the polar ice caps. Carrie and the girls had to convince the Ice Lord to return the wand and save Earth.

Rainbow Reveal

Carrie and Crystal the Snow Fairy have friendly competitions to see who can create the biggest and most sparkly snowballs!

Did you know?

The temperature at the South Pole can go as low as -65 degrees Celsius. Brrr!

Carrie's jacket is fake fur – she loves animals too much to wear real fur!

Ally
the Dolphin Fairy

Did you know?
It's often said that dolphins communicate by singing!

The girls were at the start of a seaside holiday when they received a magical invitation to the Fairyland Ocean Gala! They learned that Shannon the Ocean Fairy plays a magical tune on the Golden Conch Shell each year to make everything harmonious in all the oceans. But Jack Frost's clumsy goblins had stolen the shell and broken it into pieces. The Ocean Fairies needed Rachel and Kirsty's help!

Rainbow Reveal

Each of the seven Ocean Fairies has an ocean animal as a companion. These animals lead each fairy to a piece of the Golden Conch Shell!

Amelie
the Seal Fairy

A magical, sparkly light in a lantern led Rachel and Kirsty to Amelie! This little fairy knew her seal, Silky, was nearby, which meant the shell piece was close by, too. But so were some goblins dressed as pirates…

Did you know?

You can find seals in the UK! They are shy creatures and like quiet areas where they can sunbathe.

Pia
the Penguin Fairy

P ia took the girls on a wintry trip to the South Pole! But the girls found that everything is topsy-turvy because the conch shell hadn't been played. Even animals that live near the sea, such as polar bears, were very confused and in the wrong place!

Did you know?

Penguins are birds, but they can't fly!

Tess
the Sea Turtle Fairy

The silly goblins think that baby turtles are baby Pogwurzels!

When Tess waves her wand, lots of tiny turtles appear!

A tropical island was the setting for this fairy adventure! Tess knew that her ocean animal, a beautiful turtle called Pearl, was near the fourth piece of the missing conch shell. Rachel and Kirsty had to help get the shell piece back to Fairyland so that the chaos in the ocean could be put right. But first they had to help hundreds of baby turtles and deal with three very scared goblins!

Did you know?

Mummy turtles lay their eggs on beaches and bury them in the sand. When the babies hatch, the clever baby turtles head straight into the sea!

Stephanie
the Starfish Fairy

I n this story, it was time for the girls to enjoy a spot of stargazing. But there was only one star the girls wanted to spot – Stephanie's magical starfish, Spike!

Did you know?

There are thought to be 2,000 different species of starfish on Earth!

Whitney
the Whale Fairy

A hoy there! Rachel and Kirsty were on board an old-fashioned sailing ship when they helped Whitney. There was lots to see, including a pod of killer whales! One of the whales looked strangely sparkly, so the girls knew that a missing piece of the magical shell was close by…

Rainbow Reveal

Whitney and Flukey patrol the seas making sure every whale is safe and happy.

Courtney
the Clownfish Fairy

I t was almost time for Rachel and Kirsty's holiday to end when they met Courtney and her clownfish, Tickle. They visited a magical underwater funfair, but Jack Frost and lots of goblins were also at the fair searching for the Golden Conch Shell!

Did you know?
Clownfish are really small! The biggest they can grow is 18 centimetres long.

Rainbow Reveal

When Courtney appears in the story, she's inside a fish-shaped balloon!

Rainbow Reveal

At the end of their ocean adventures the girls are given a beautiful conch shell as a gift from Queen Titania and King Oberon.

Ava
the Sunset Fairy

The Twilight Fairies have such a special job, using their magic fairy dust to make sure that everything is looked after between dusk and dawn. Kirsty and Rachel were visiting Camp Stargaze for a week with their families when they spotted a very strange green sunset…they just knew it was to do with Jack Frost! First of all they had to help Ava find her missing bag of sunbeam dust.

Lexi
the Firefly Fairy

The girls went on a night-time stroll to the twinkling tree in this story, but with Lexi's bag of magic twilight dust missing, the twinkling tree was not living up to its name…

Did you know?
Fireflies are also known as 'lightning bugs' because of the flashes of light they produce!

Zara
the Starlight Fairy

Rachel and Kirsty spotted a strange constellation in Camp Stargaze's observatory at the start of this story! With Zara's bag of star dust missing, the stars were up to all sorts of odd things…

Did you know?
A constellation is a group of stars that look like a dot-to-dot puzzle!

Morgan
the Midnight Fairy

Rainbow Reveal

In this story, the goblins are having an amazing feast of their own with the help of Morgan's magic fairy dust.

Some of the best parties are held at midnight, and Morgan makes sure they are always exciting with the help of her enchanted night dust. But when her magical dust went missing, everything started to go wrong. The fire wouldn't light, the marshmallows wouldn't roast and the midnight stories all had the wrong endings!

Rainbow Reveal

Morgan's dress is the colour of the night sky at midnight!

Yasmin
the Night Owl Fairy

All sorts of animals are awake at night-time, but with Yasmin's magic bag missing, the behaviour of night-time and daytime animals went all topsy-turvy!

Maisie
the Moonbeam Fairy

Moonlight is the most magical of lights, but in Maisie's story the silly goblins tried to make their own moon! It was up to the girls and Maisie to stop them and return Maisie's moon dust to her.

Twilight Fairies

Sabrina
the Sweet Dreams Fairy

Sabrina has such an important job – she makes sure that everyone has sweet dreams rather than nightmares! But she needs her magical dream dust to do this. Once, her bag fell into the hands of the goblins, and nobody in the human world or Fairyland could sleep peacefully!

Did you know?

Everybody dreams, even Jack Frost and the goblins!

Without her dream dust, Sabrina has been known to sleep-fly!

Rainbow Reveal

Sabrina sometimes sings a lovely lullaby that puts everyone to sleep!

Madison
the Magic Show Fairy

The Showtime Fairies' magic stars help everyone to make the most of their special skill or talent.

In this story, the goblins use Madison's wand to cause lots of trouble at the magic show auditions.

It was October half-term and almost time for the Tippington Variety Show when the girls met Madison! They were really looking forward to watching all the different acts practise and perform. But when the girls discovered that Madison's wand had been stolen, they knew the variety show would be lacking some very important magic…

Leah
the Theatre Fairy

Rachel's school was rehearsing for a performance of Cinderella in the beautiful Swan Theatre in Leah's story! The school was hoping to get to the finals of the Tippington Variety Show. But everything was going wrong because of Leah's missing star…

Did you know?

The most famous fairy in theatre is Shakespeare's Queen Titania.

Alesha
the Acrobat Fairy

It's Alesha's job to make sure that everyone taking part in acrobatic shows performs well and has lots of fun. But this can only happen when she has her magic star…

Rainbow Reveal

Alesha's bright pink leotard has magical fairy dust sewn into it!

Darcey
the Dance Diva Fairy

The girls visited the Funky Feet dance studio in this story! Rachel's school was auditioning for a place in the Tippington Variety Show with an amazing hip-hop dance routine. But, with Darcey's star missing, there was nothing amazing about it, and all the other schools' routines were going horribly wrong, too!

Rainbow Reveal

Jack Frost wanted the goblins to hide the magic stars in the human world so that nobody showed any talents.

Darcey's stunning dress is in the style of the 1920s! The fringes sway and shake when she dances.

Amelia
the Singing Fairy

Amelia's magic star allows true singing talent to shine, but when it fell into the hands of the goblins everything went topsy-turvy and the pesky creatures had all the singing talent instead!

Isla
the Ice Star Fairy

Ice-skating is such a special skill and practice really does make perfect! But no matter how much the competitors rehearsed in this story, their routines weren't getting any better. The girls knew they had to find Isla's magic star!

Taylor
the Talent Show Fairy

In Taylor's tale, it was time for the Tippington Variety Show to begin. Jack Frost came to the show personally to make sure that Taylor's magic star wasn't returned to her. Her star makes sure shows run smoothly, and Jack Frost wanted to ruin the show for everyone!

Rainbow Reveal

Jack Frost discovers that he can tell great jokes in this story!

The Showtime Fairies have help from the Dance Fairies and Music Fairies to perfect their talents.

Honor
the Happy Days Fairy

Rachel and Kirsty are invited to a ball, But Jack Frost tries to ruin it all!

Rainbow Reveal

The Queen's magic sent the missing tiaras to Golden Palace.

Rachel and Kirsty were spending a week at Golden Palace when they met the Princess Fairies. It's a magical old castle where real princes and princesses once lived! The girls were whisked away to a Fairyland Ball by Polly the Party Fun Fairy. But mean Jack Frost gate-crashed the ball and stole the royal fairies' tiaras! Without the tiaras, no human or fairy would ever have a happy time again.

Did you know?

The oldest castle in England is the Tower of London, where the girls meet Elizabeth the Jubilee Fairy!

Demi
the Dressing-Up Fairy

Did you know?

A pageant is a magnificent display that tells a story.

The girls and their friends enjoyed exploring Golden Palace in Demi's story – but they soon had to help Demi find her tiara, so everyone could look beautiful at the pageant.

Anya
the Cuddly Creatures Fairy

Golden Palace has its own petting zoo and there are lots of different animals to meet there! But with Anya's golden tiara in the hands of the goblins, all the cuddly creatures behave very oddly…

Rainbow Reveal

Anya's magic helps keep the special friendship between animals and humans strong.

Elisa
the Adventure Fairy

W ith Elisa's sparkly tiara missing, nobody wanted to have any fun! The girls had to track down the goblins to put things right. In this story, everyone apart from Rachel and Kirsty lost their sense of adventure.

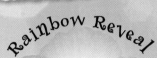

Rainbow Reveal

Elisa's magic makes the spirit of fun and adventure strong in every human and fairy.

Elisa often organises trips and treasure hunts for her fairy friends.

Each of the Princess Fairies' tiaras has a different-shaped jewel.

Lizzie
the Sweet Treats Fairy

It was time for a royal tea party at Golden Palace and everyone was looking forward to having lots of delicious things to eat. But without Princess Lizzie's golden tiara to make sure everything tasted delicious, all of the sweet treats were sure to be awful!

Rainbow Reveal

Lizzie often swaps recipes with Cherry the Cake Fairy and Honey the Sweet Fairy. Yummy!

Maddie
the Playtime Fairy

Maddie the Playtime Fairy makes sure that children everywhere enjoy games and playtime! But with her magic tiara missing, everyone at Golden Palace was very miserable. Rachel and Kirsty had to find the tiara before the sports day was ruined!

Rainbow Reveal

Maddie is riding a rocking horse when the girls discover her!

Eva
the Enchanted Ball Fairy

Rainbow Reveal

Rachel and Kirsty enjoy two wonderful balls – one at Golden Palace and the other at the Fairyland Palace.

Rainbow Reveal

Jack Frost is such a troublemaker that the fairies have stopped inviting him to their parties!

Eva's special magic makes sure that everyone is beautifully dressed for special parties and balls. But whilst Eva's tiara is with Jack Frost, celebrations everywhere will be a disaster. In this story Rachel and Kirsty had to visit the scary Ice Castle, to take Eva's tiara back from the Ice Lord!

Jessie
the Lyrics Fairy

The girls were so excited to return to Rainspell Island for a five-day music festival! But when they got there, they found out that mean Jack Frost had stolen the Pop Star Fairies' magical clef necklaces. Without Jessie's necklace, none of the stars singing at pop events anywhere would remember their words!

Rainbow Reveal

Jessie's pink boots were a present from Phoebe the Fashion Fairy.

Jessie loves using her imagination to write song lyrics.

Adele
the Singing Coach Fairy

Adele's magic helps pop stars in Fairyland and the human world sing on key! But with her magic necklace missing, no one could strike the right notes at the music festival. Well, apart from a mysterious new pop star called Gobby…

Rainbow Reveal

In Adele's story the girls get to meet to meet their favourite ever boy band, A-OK!

Vanessa
the Dance Steps Fairy

Being able to dance is a very important part of being a pop star! Vanessa helps each star perfect their routines. In her story, it was almost time for pop sensation Sasha Sharp to perform, but Sasha couldn't dance a single step!

Rainbow Reveal

Vanessa's blue playsuit was handmade by Tyra the Dress Designer Fairy.

Miley
the Stylist Fairy

Miley's magic helps pop stars look their very best. But at the Rainspell Festival, Miley's necklace went missing, so all the pop stars' clothes and accessories were in a terrible mess…

Rainbow Reveal

Jack Frost thinks he knows everything about fashion – take a peek at the Fashion Fairies books to find out more!

Did you know?
Fashion stylists select clothing for TV ads and magazine pictures, as well as for pop performances!

Miley is always on the lookout for the hottest new trend.

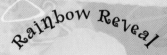

Frankie
the Make-Up Fairy

H aving your face painted at a festival is always great fun. But when Frankie's necklace went missing at the Rainspell event, all face paint and make-up looked horrible!

Rainbow Reveal

Frankie was in the same class at school as Miranda the Beauty Fairy.

Rochelle
the Star Spotter Fairy

R ochelle's skill is very special to all pop sensations – she spots new stars and makes sure that every one of them feels full of confidence. But with her magical clef in the hands of the goblins at the Rainspell Festival, the search for new talent seemed to be over… until the girls saved the day!

Rainbow Reveal

Taylor the Talent Show Fairy shares her secret talent-spotting tips with Rochelle.

Una
the Concert Fairy

Rainbow Reveal

A magical music festival takes place in Fairyland at the same time as the Rainspell Music Festival!

U na's magic clef necklace makes sure concerts run smoothly, so with it missing, the final concert of the Rainspell Music Festival went horribly wrong... The girls had to trick Jack Frost into returning the necklace so there could be a fabulous festival finale!

Jack Frost's stage name is Jax Tempo.

Una loves orange chocolate-chip cookies.

Miranda
the Beauty Fairy

These fairies make fashion trendy and new. They help natural beauty to shine brightly through!

Did you know?

Queen Elizabeth II has her own special lipstick called The Balmoral Lipstick. It was made to match her coronation robes.

Rainbow Reveal

Miranda has over 100 lipsticks in her make-up collection!

W hen a brand-new shopping centre opened in Tippington, Kirsty and Rachel decided to enter a charity fashion show where they could design their own clothes. But mean Jack Frost was up to his old tricks again. He thought everyone in the world should dress like him, so he stole the seven Fashion Fairies' magical items – including Miranda's shimmery magical lipstick – to put his plan into action!

Claudia
the Accessories Fairy

I t's lovely to have a pretty accessory to match an outfit! But with Claudia's magic necklace in the hands of Jack Frost and his goblins, accessories everywhere fell apart and lost their sparkle…

Rainbow Reveal

Claudia always matches her hairband to her shoes!

Tyra
the Dress Designer Fairy

I n Tyra's story, it was time for the girls to get creative at the Design-and-Make workshop! But with Tyra's magical tape measure missing, all the clothes in the Tippington Fountains Shopping Centre were falling apart!

Rainbow Reveal

Tyra likes to design new dresses with Miley the Stylist Fairy!

Alexa
the Fashion Reporter Fairy

Did you know?

The most famous fashion magazine is called Vogue.

J ack Frost was determined to let everyone know about his crazy new fashion label, Ice Blue, and he used the magic of Alexa's stolen pen to do it! The girls had to track down the missing magical item before Jack Frost could become the most famous fashion designer in the human world.

Rainbow Reveal

Jack Frost is so silly and vain that in Alexa's story he interviews himself about his own fashion label!

Alexa and Hannah the Happy Ever After Fairy both use their magical pens to write stories for the Fairyland News.

Matilda
the Hair Stylist Fairy

When your hair has been styled nicely, it makes you feel very special! But without Matilda's special magic, scissors blunt and in this story, everyone's hair turned a strange shade of blue!

Rainbow Reveal

Matilda's top hair-care tip is to keep your locks clean and knot-free!

Rainbow Reveal

Brooke's hobby is to cut up photos she's taken, and make them into collages for her friends!

Brooke
the Photographer Fairy

Rachel and Kirsty were taking part in a fashion photoshoot when Brooke appeared! Brooke's magic camera was missing, and when Jack Frost started acting like a stroppy model, the girls had a suspicion where the camera might be...

Lola
the Fashion Show Fairy

I n this final Fashion Fairy adventure, it was time for the Tippington Fountains fashion show! Kirsty and Rachel couldn't wait to be part of the fun and model their own designs on the catwalk. But Lola's magical backstage pass went missing, and the girls knew that without it, the fashion show would be a spectacular disaster!

Did you know?

Each year designers hold big fashion shows in New York, Paris, Milan and London to showcase the next season's designs.

Rainbow Reveal

Lola's sparkly silver boots are perfect for a night out dancing with Jade the Disco Fairy!

Holly
the Christmas Fairy

Kirsty and Rachel met Holly on a trip to Fairyland just before Christmas, when they discovered that Jack Frost had stolen Santa's sleigh! Without it, Santa couldn't deliver any presents to boys and girls in the human world. Holly needed the girls' help to find her three magical Christmas presents and put things right.

Holly gives Santa's reindeer flying lessons every year!

Rainbow Reveal

Holly's scarlet dress was made for her by Santa's elves. It's made from the same material as Santa's robes!

Did you know?
Santa and his reindeer travel 75.5 million miles on Christmas Eve!

Summer
the Holiday Fairy

Every vacation should be full of fun. But mean Jack Frost upsets everyone!

Did you know?

Summer's birthday is in August! Her birthstone is the lovely green peridot.

Rachel and Kirsty were so excited to be returning to Rainspell Island for a summer holiday! But things weren't how they remembered them at all…the sea was rough, the beach wasn't sandy and even the ice cream tasted horrid! The girls had to help Summer find her Rainspell shells and make summer holidays fun for everyone once again!

Rainbow Reveal

When Summer uses her wand, lovely summery smells waft in the air!

Jack Frost stole the Rainspell shells because he didn't want anyone else to have a nice holiday.

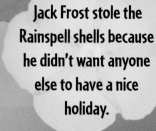

Stella
the Star Fairy

Stella's a bright
and Christmassy star,
Bringing joy, love and light
wherever you are!

Did you know?

There are 300 billion stars in the Milky Way!

Each year, Stella the Star Fairy uses her three magic Christmas tree decorations to make sure that everyone's Christmas is shining and bright. But when mean Jack Frost stole the magic decorations, the special time of year looked like being dark and miserable for everyone…

Rainbow Reveal

Stella and Holly work together to help all the other fairies decorate their homes!

Stella the Star Fairy and Holly the Christmas Fairy are best friends!

Kylie
the Carnival Fairy

Sunnydays Carnival only comes to town once a year and everyone has a brilliant time going on the rides, playing games and watching the parades. But the year Rachel and Kirsty met Kylie, Jack Frost and his goblins were at the carnival too! The pesky creatures stole Kylie's three magic hats and everything started to go wrong. The girls had to move quickly and help Kylie outwit the mean Ice Lord and his goblin servants.

Rainbow Reveal

Did you know?

One of the biggest carnivals in the world is held each year in the Brazilian city of Rio de Janeiro. Over 500,000 people visit the city to join in the fun.

Kylie's outfit showcases all the joy and fun of the carnival! Her skirt twirls in a rainbow of colour and the ribbons in her hair dance in the breeze.

Paige
the Pantomime Fairy

When Jack Frost steals Paige's magic shoes, Everyone gets the pantomime blues!

When they met Paige, Kirsty and Rachel were due to perform in Cinderella. But things were not going well. Paige's three magic shoes were missing, so the costumes didn't fit, the scenery was breaking, and nobody could remember their lines!

Did you know?

Pantomimes are thought to have begun in Roman times.

Rainbow Reveal

Paige's favourite ever pantomime is Sleeping Beauty!

101

Flora
the Fancy Dress Fairy

The crown of shells worn by Flora was made for her by Shannon the Ocean Fairy.

I n this magical story, Kirsty and Rachel were staying in a real castle! Kirsty's cousin, Lindsay, was throwing a wonderful fancy-dress ball. The girls couldn't wait to get dressed up! But when they stumbled across Jack Frost at the castle, they knew Lindsay's ball was in trouble. They needed Flora's help – and she needed their help to protect her three magic items from the naughty goblins!

Rainbow Reveal

Flora's favourite spell is to turn old clothes into perfect party outfits!

Flora's magic items are a figurine, a cape and a mask. They make sure that all parties go without a hitch.

Chrissie
the Wish Fairy

Chrissie's wish magic allows a person holding one of her magical objects to have their wish come true. But when Rachel and Kirsty met Chrissie, her magic Christmas card, carol sheet and wooden spoon had all been stolen!

Rainbow Reveal

Chrissie has a wish of her own – one day she'd love to help Santa deliver presents to children all over the world!

Chrissie adores wrapping presents with Jasmine the Present Fairy. They always make gifts look extra-special.

We Wish You A Merry Christmas

Shannon
the Ocean Fairy

Shannon loses her enchanted pearls, And tries to find them with help from the girls!

The girls were visiting Kirsty's gran in the seaside town of Leamouth when they were magically invited to a Fairyland beach party! Here they met flame-haired Shannon – who told them that Jack Frost had stolen her three enchanted pearls!

Rainbow Reveal

Shannon magics two bubbles to go over Rachel and Kirsty's heads to let them breathe and speak underwater!

Lucky Shannon is friends with all of the ocean creatures and the Ocean Fairies!

104

Gabriella
the Snow Kingdom Fairy

Rachel and Kirsty were having a wonderful snowy holiday in the mountains when they met Gabriella! They were really looking forward to skiing, snowboarding and going to the Winter Festival. But no such luck – everything seemed to be going wrong! Gabriella needed Rachel and Kirsty's help to find her magic snowflake, chest full of festive spirit, and firestone, so she could put things right...

Rainbow Reveal

Gabriella and Crystal the Snow Fairy are best of friends!

The Winter Olympics happen every four years – Gabriella is always there!

105

Mia
the Bridesmaid Fairy

Brides should carry something old, something new, something borrowed and something blue!

Rachel and Kirsty were counting down the days until they were bridesmaids for Kirsty's cousin Esther! Preparations were going very well but a visit from Mia the Bridesmaid Fairy changed everything – something was wrong with her three magical wedding charms. The girls had to help Mia so that Esther's wedding wasn't a total disaster…

Rainbow Reveal

Mia's wedding charms are a silver sixpence, golden bells and a moonshine veil!

Mia is great friends with Kate the Royal Wedding Fairy.

Destiny
the Pop Star
Fairy

Rainbow Reveal

Rachel and Kirsty's favourite girl group is The Angels!

Destiny the Pop Star Fairy has a very fun job – she makes sure that pop music everywhere sounds fantastic!

Destiny works closely with the seven Pop Star Fairies to look after all pop music!

Destiny's three magical objects are the sparkle sash, which perfects pop stars' outfits; the keepsake key, which looks after all songs and music; and the magical microphone, which makes sound and lighting work brilliantly! But mean Jack Frost once stole these magical items from the pop princess as he wanted to be the best pop star in town…

Belle
the Birthday Fairy

Dressed in purple with a flower in her hair, Belle tries her best to make birthdays fun and fair!

In Belle's story, Rachel and her dad had planned a surprise birthday party for Rachel's mum. But nothing seemed to be going right for anyone's special day and the two girls knew something was wrong in Fairyland…they needed to help Belle make birthdays brilliant once more!

Rainbow Reveal

Belle and the Party Fairies are always working together to make every fairy's special day magical in every way.

Jack Frost hates birthdays because he doesn't want anyone to know how old he is!

Juliet
the Valentine Fairy

A gorgeous red rose is often a sign of a lovely, romantic Valentine!

Who on earth doesn't like Valentine's Day? Jack Frost, that's who! He tried to ruin it one year by stealing Juliet's magical objects. With these objects in the hands of the silly goblins – plus a wand to cause *extra* trouble – the magic of Valentine's Day looked sure to be destroyed.

Rainbow Reveal

Juliet's magical objects are a Valentine's card, a red rose and a box of chocolate hearts.

It's traditional to send cards to people you love on Valentine's Day!

Trixie
the Halloween Fairy

The goblins have stolen all the Halloween sweets, so this day will be full of tricks but no treats!

Rachel and Kirsty couldn't wait to go trick-or-treating in Tippington! Every year, the children dress up and have a really fun time. But a visit from Trixie the Halloween Fairy put the girls on high alert – the greedy goblins had stolen her three Halloween sweets and with them missing, nobody could have any spooky fun.

Did you know?

Halloween was originally a British holiday called 'Samhain'. It was celebrated by the Celts, who lived during the Iron Age.

Rainbow Reveal

With Trixie, the girls meet a little black kitten called Moonlight.

Cheryl
the Christmas Tree Fairy

Cheryl's magic
helps to make
Christmas really
special.

Decorating a Christmas tree is such an important part of Christmas! In this story Rachel and Kirsty discovered that Cheryl's Fairyland Christmas tree was missing. This special tree looks after lots of different areas of the festive season and with it missing, the Christmas time celebrations couldn't begin…

Jack Frost has taken
Cheryl's magic objects
because he wants his
Christmas to be the only
one that's any fun!

Cheryl also has a
magical Christmas star
and Christmas gift.

Rainbow Reveal

Florence
the Friendship Fairy

Everyone knows just how important friendship is, so Florence really is a very special fairy! Her three magic objects look after all aspects of friendship – her memory book keeps happy memories safe, her friendship ribbon lets friends have lots of fun, and her sparkly bracelet protects all friendships. But when Florence once lost her objects, Kirsty and Rachel had to use their special friendship to save the day.

Rainbow Reveal

In this story Florence and the other fairies make Rachel and Kirsty a very special friendship bracelet each, to say thank you for being such brilliant pals!

Rainbow Reveal

Every year, Florence organises a special Friendship Day, to celebrate friendships everywhere!

112

Emma
the Easter Fairy

Emma makes
Easter lots of fun,
With chocolate eggs
for everyone!

Rainbow Reveal

Emma's pet chicken,
Fluffy, lays her three
magic eggs every
year!

Did you know?

The custom of giving
eggs at Easter time goes back
to the Ancient Egyptians and
Romans. They saw the egg as
a symbol of life.

A visit from Emma one year soon threatened Rachel and Kirsty's happy holiday – the Easter bunny had gone missing and Emma's three magic eggs had been stolen! The girls had to help out, before Easter was ruined.

Kate
the Royal Wedding Fairy

K ate has such a special job – she makes sure that all weddings are bursting with love and joy! When there was a royal wedding in Fairyland, mean Jack Frost stole Kate's True Love Crown. Rachel and Kirsty had to help her find it quickly, so the royal couple could live happily ever after!

Rainbow Reveal

Kate the Royal Wedding Fairy is best friends with Mia the Bridesmaid Fairy!

Kate's shoes have amazing diamonds on the toes. They were a gift from Elizabeth the Jubilee Fairy.

Selena
the Sleepover Fairy

Selena's tip for sleepovers is to make a door hanger, so your family know when you and your friends are busy!

S elena's job is to make all sleepovers great fun! When Rachel and Kirsty went to a big sleepover at a museum, strange things started to happen. The girls suspected it had something to do with a naughty group of children with green skin and very big noses... They helped Selena as best they could!

Selena often spends time with Sabrina the Sweet Dreams Fairy, swapping tips.

Selena's three magic objects are a sleeping bag, a games bag and a snack box.

Hannah
the Happy Ever After Fairy

Hannah's magic quill pen
fills stories with joy,
So reading is fun for each
girl and boy!

In this special story the endings of favourite fairy tales were changed, so there were no happy-ever-afters! Hannah needed Kirsty and Rachel to help her find out what was going wrong. She knew it had something to do with mean Jack Frost and her missing quill pen…

Rainbow Reveal

Whenever Hannah uses her magic pen, rainbow-coloured sparkles fizz from the end of it.

Jack Frost uses the magic quill to make fairy tales have sad endings. What a meanie!

Natalie
the Christmas Stocking Fairy

Natalie's keeps her magical items in a beautiful white box with a gold clasp.

N atalie's special fairy magic makes sure opening presents from Christmas stockings is a time full of joy and happiness. But without her magical stocking, mince pie and candy cane, Natalie couldn't make Christmas morning magical… or any other part of Christmas Day!

Rainbow Reveal

Natalie's wand spills glittery silver snowflakes from the tip whenever she casts a spell.

Hanging up stockings is a Victorian tradition. Santa only fills them with presents if you've been very well behaved!

Keira
the Film Star Fairy

Keira's magic looks after each bright movie star. With her help and training, each actor will go far!

Rainbow Reveal

Rochelle the Star Spotter Fairy was the one who spotted Keira's flair for film!

Tyra the Dress Designer Fairy designed Keira's long red silk dress.

FILM SCRIPT

PROD. SLM TAKE

When Rachel and Kirsty met Keira, they were extras in a real Hollywood movie being filmed in Tippington! Things started to go wrong on set, and the girls soon received a visit from a very glamorous little fairy who had lost her silver script, magical megaphone and enchanted clapperboard.

Olympia
the Games Fairy

This special fairy has the perfect sporting name. She'll always do her best to help you win your favourite game!

Olympia is the sportiest fairy in Fairyland! She uses her magic to make sure that sporting games and tournaments in the human world and Fairyland are fun, organised and – above all – fair!

Rainbow Reveal

Olympia's magic objects are a sparkling swimming cap, a musical bicycle bell and a pair of tireless trainers.

Olympia's magic watches over the Melford Triathlon, the Fairyland Games and the Fairyland Olympics!

Rainbow Reveal

119

Elizabeth
the Jubilee Fairy

Elizabeth is a fairy who glitters, shines and glows. She sparkles like a diamond from her head down to her toes!

Elizabeth is a very important fairy – she makes sure that all jubilee celebrations are perfect. Rachel and Kirsty met Elizabeth in the Tower of London, and had to travel to Fairyland, and the chilly goblin village, to help her out!

Did you know?

Queen Elizabeth the Second's Diamond Jubilee celebrates her 60 years on the throne.

Rainbow Reveal

Elizabeth's dress has thousands of tiny diamonds stitched onto it.

Tamara
the Tooth Fairy

When Jack Frost had terrible toothache, he stole Tamara's magical moonstone ring, endless coin and enchanted pouch to try and make himself feel better. But without her objects, Tamara couldn't do her job properly and children all over the human world suffered!

Rainbow Reveal

Zara the Starlight Fairy lights Tamara's way to lost teeth.

Rainbow Reveal

Tamara loves chatting to night-time creatures!

BANK OF MAGIC

Angelica
the Angel Fairy

Angelica is good and kind, and uses her magic to keep Christmas time peaceful. That is, unless Jack Frost steals her magical pan pipes, snow-white feather and enchanted name scroll! When Rachel and Kirsty met Angelica, this was just what had happened!

In total, there are 7 Christmas fairies.

The Christmas fairies always spend Christmas Eve together!

Rainbow Reveal

I was the first fairy that Rachel and
Kirsty found, and I am so glad they did!
The girls have helped all the Rainbow
Magic fairies so much, and we look upon
them as our very special friends.

We fairies do not show ourselves easily to humans, and
when we do it is only ever to children. It was just a lucky
chance Rachel and Kirsty met me during their holiday
to Rainspell Island. It could just have easily been you.

Always keep a look out for fairies wherever you are.
Peep inside flowers, look right into the corners of frosty
windows, check in the bottom of your dressing-up box,
and even in the folds of the curtains in your bedroom.
You never know when we may need your help.

I hope we will meet you one day.
We love to visit the human world.

Lots of love,
Ruby xxx

Have you read them all?

The Rainbow Fairies

The Weather Fairies

The Party Fairies

The Jewel Fairies

The Pet Keeper Fairies

The Fun Day Fairies

The
Petal Fairies

The
Dance Fairies

The
Sporty Fairies

The
Music Fairies

The Magical
Animal Fairies

The
Green Fairies

The
Ocean Fairies

The
Twilight Fairies

The
Showtime Fairies

The
Princess Fairies

The
Pop Star Fairies

The
Fashion Fairies